Robots Everywhere

Description

After sharing what they know about different types of robots, students model how robots are programmed to perform tasks. They learn that every robot is designed for a specific job, and that job determines what a robot looks like. They also design a solution to a simple problem by creating a labeled drawing of a robot that could complete a particular task in their own home or at school.

Alignment With the *Next Generation Science Standards*

Performance Expectations

K-2-ETS1-1: Ask questions, make observations, and gather information about a situation people want to change to define a simple problem that can be solved through the development of a new or improved object or tool.

K-2-ETS1-2: Develop a simple sketch, drawing, or physical model to illustrate how the shape of an object helps it function as needed to solve a given problem.

Science and Engineering Practices	Disciplinary Core Ideas	Crosscutting Concept
Developing and Using Models Develop a simple model based on evidence to represent a proposed object or tool. Distinguish between a model and the actual object, process, and/or events the model represents. **Constructing Explanations and Designing Solutions** Use tools and/or materials to design and/or build a device that solves a specific problem or a solution to a specific problem.	**ETS1.A: Defining and Delimiting Engineering Problems** A situation that people want to change or create can be approached as a problem to be solved through engineering. Asking questions, making observations, and gathering information are helpful in thinking about problems. Before beginning to design a solution, it is important to clearly understand the problem.	**Structure and Function** The shape and stability of structures of natural and designed objects are related to their function(s). **Influence of Engineering, Technology, and Science on Society and the Natural World** People depend on various technologies in their lives; human life would be very different without technology.

Continued

Alignment With the Next Generation Science Standards *(continued)*

Science and Engineering Practices	Disciplinary Core Ideas	Crosscutting Concept
Planning and Carrying Out Investigations Make observations (firsthand or from media) and/or measurements of a proposed object or tool or solution to determine if it solves a problem or meets a goal.	**ETS1.B: Developing Possible Solutions** Designs can be conveyed through sketches, drawings, or physical models. These representations are useful in communicating ideas for a problem's solutions to other people.	

Note: The activities in this lesson will help students move toward the performance expectations listed, which is the goal after multiple activities. However, the activities will not by themselves be sufficient to reach the performance expectations.

Contemporary research on how students learn science, reflected in the *Next Generation Science Standards* and other state standards based in *A Framework for K–12 Science Education,* requires that engineering lessons taught as part of the science curriculum provide students with opportunities to "acquire and use elements of disciplinary core ideas from physical, life, or Earth and space sciences together with elements of disciplinary core ideas from engineering design to solve design problems" (NGSS Lesson Screener, *www.nextgenscience.org/screener*). While the "Robots Everywhere" lesson does provide opportunities for students to build ideas in science and engineering, it does not meet this requirement.

Featured Picture Books

TITLE:	***Beep! Beep! Go to Sleep!***
AUTHOR:	**Todd Tarpley**
ILLUSTRATOR:	**John Rocco**
PUBLISHER:	**Little, Brown Books for Young Readers**
YEAR:	**2015**
GENRE:	**Story**
SUMMARY:	*This fun, rhyming story will have kids giggling as a little boy tries everything to get his household robots to power down.*

TITLE:	***National Geographic Kids: Robots***
AUTHOR:	**Melissa Stewart**
PUBLISHER:	**National Geographic Children's Books**
YEAR:	**2014**
GENRE:	**Non-Narrative Information**
SUMMARY:	*Young readers will learn about the most fascinating robots of today and tomorrow in this colorful, photo-packed book.*

Time Needed

This lesson will take several class periods. Suggested scheduling is as follows:

Session 1: **Engage** with *Beep! Beep! Go to Sleep!* Read-Aloud, **Explore** with Robot Arms, and **Explain** with Robot Arms Discussion and Chocolate Factory Video

Session 2: **Explain** with *National Geographic Kids: Robots* Read-Aloud and Robot Jobs Card Sort

Session 3: **Elaborate** with Robots of the Future and **Evaluate** with My Robot

Materials

For Robot Arms (per pair)

- 9 × 12 in. two-pocket folder with a mouse-hole-shaped opening (large enough for a student's arm to reach through) cut in the bottom center
- 1 small bowl
- Plastic zipper bag with about 10 pieces of spiral-shaped pasta and about 10 pieces of tube-shaped or bowtie pasta
- 1 precut Robot Arm Program Card

Optional: For My Robot Advertisement (per student)

- White poster board or large construction paper
- Markers

SAFETY

- Check with your school nurse about wheat allergies, and substitute wheat-free pasta if necessary.
- Remind students not to eat any food used in the lab or activity.
- Caution students not to put the plastic bag in or over their noses and mouths to prevent breathing issues.
- Wash hands with soap and water after completing this activity.

Student Pages

- Robot Jobs Card Sort
- Robot Job Descriptions
- My Robot and My Robot Advertisement
- STEM Everywhere

Background for Teachers

What do you think of when you hear the word *robot*? Most likely, you have a mental image of a walking, talking, blinking, and thinking humanoid machine. But most robots don't really look like people at all. Robots come in every shape and size you can think of and perform more jobs than you can imagine. If it seems as if robots are everywhere today, that's because they are! In this lesson, students learn about the influence of engineering, technology, and science on society by studying how people have come to depend on robots to do many jobs they could not (or would not) do.

So what exactly is a robot? Oddly enough, there is no widely accepted, standard definition of a robot. Even Joseph Engelberger, often referred to as the "father" of the modern robotics industry, was said to have remarked, "I can't define a robot, but I know one when I see it." In *National Geographic Kids: Robots,* author Melissa Stewart proposes this definition: "A robot, or bot, is a *machine* that has movable parts and can make decisions. People design it to do a job by itself." Although some robots lack

computers and perform only simple, motor-driven tasks, the book explains that most robots have three main types of parts: a computer, sensors, and actuators. A robot's *computer* contains programs to help it make decisions. It makes these decisions based on data collected by its *sensors*. Some common robot sensors are video cameras to "see"; microphones to "hear"; pressure and temperature sensors to "feel"; ultrasound, infrared, and laser sensors to measure distance, navigate, and avoid obstacles; and even sensors that detect magnetic fields and certain types of chemicals.

INDUSTRIAL ROBOT ARM

To be called a robot, a machine must move. *Actuators,* also known as drives, are devices that receive messages from the computer and control the robot's movements. Most actuators are powered by pneumatics (air pressure), hydraulics (fluid pressure), or motors (electric current), but they all convert one kind of energy into motion energy. Actuators help the robot make sounds, flash lights, pick things up, move, and so on. Sometimes the whole robot moves, like the rovers that are rolling around the surface of Mars collecting rock samples and other data. Sometimes the robot is stationary with moving parts, like the robotic arms commonly used in industry for many different kinds of jobs. Welding or spray-painting robots don't have to move from place to place, but when a robot's job does require movement, robotics engineers (or *roboticists*) usually design it to have tracks, wheels, or legs (and some robots can even swim or fly). Robots need energy to move. They might be plugged in, battery powered, or even solar powered, depending on what they are designed to do.

In this lesson, students learn that a robot can only do things that engineers and roboticists *program* it to do. They learn that a robot's programming must be very detailed; each and every step must be spelled out for a robot to do its job properly. They model how a "pick-and-place" industrial robot arm needs a very precise and logical *program* to follow in order to complete a task, such as picking things up and sorting them. To model this, each student "programs" his or her partner's "robot arm" to pick up and sort pasta shapes into separate piles. In this activity, students are engaged in the science and engineering practice (SEP) of developing and using models as they compare their model robot arm to a video of an actual robot arm in action.

Students also learn that most robots are designed to do jobs that are too repetitive or dangerous for humans to do. Robots can explore places that humans can't go, such as Mars, the deepest trenches of the sea, or the craters of active volcanoes. But some of the handiest robots have less glamorous jobs: they are the domestic, or household, robots. There are robots to mow your lawn, clean your gutters, scoop out your cat's litterbox, entertain you, and even wake you up! Caregiving robots are being designed to help people with physical challenges move from a chair to a bed, fetch household items, or take a bath.

In this lesson, students also look around their homes and classrooms and brainstorm problems that robots could solve. They design a robot and then compare its strengths and weaknesses with those of the technology (or the person!) currently solving the problem. This engages them in the SEP of constructing explanations and designing solutions. Students share their designs through labeled drawings. Finally, they create an advertisement to "sell" their robot, explaining how it is a better solution than the technology (or person) currently solving the problem. The crosscutting concept (CCC) of structure

and function is woven throughout the lesson as students explore how a robot's job determines what it looks like.

In the *explore* phase, students will get a sense of how robots are programmed by being exposed to simple IF-THEN-ELSE statements. Programming is a great way to teach problem-solving, creativity, and communication skills, and even very young children can be taught simple coding. To find out more about teaching young students to code, visit Code.org, a nonprofit organization working to ensure that every student in every school has the opportunity to learn computer science. This completely free curriculum for ages 4 and up consists of multiple courses, each of which has several lessons that may be implemented as one unit or over the course of a school year. Code.org also offers free professional development workshops for elementary teachers. We hope that by learning about "robots everywhere," you and your students will be inspired to learn more about the wonderful world of coding!

Learning Progressions

Below are the disciplinary core idea (DCI) grade band endpoints for grades K–2 and 3–5. These are provided to show how student understanding of the DCIs in this lesson will progress in future grade levels.

DCIs	Grades K–2	Grades 3–5
ETS1.A: Defining and Delimiting Engineering Problems	• A situation that people want to change or create can be approached as a problem to be solved through engineering. Such problems may have many acceptable solutions. • Asking questions, making observations, and gathering information are helpful in thinking about problems. • Before beginning to design a solution, it is important to clearly understand the problem.	• Possible solutions to a problem are limited by available materials and resources (constraints). The success of a designed solution is determined by considering the desired features of the solution (criteria). Different proposals for solutions can be compared on the basis of how well each meets the specified criteria for success or how well each takes the constraints into account.
ETS1.B: Developing Possible Solutions	• Designs can be conveyed through sketches, drawings, or physical models. These representations are useful for communicating ideas for a problem's solutions to other people.	• At whatever stage, communicating with peers about proposed solutions is an important part of the design process, and shared ideas can lead to improved designs.

Source: Willard, T., ed. 2015. The NSTA quick-reference guide to the NGSS: Elementary school. Arlington, VA: NSTA Press.

engage

Beep! Beep! Go to Sleep! Read-Aloud

ENGAGING WITH BEEP! BEEP! GO TO SLEEP!

 **Inferring**

Show students the cover of *Beep! Beep! Go to Sleep!* and introduce the author, Todd Tarpley, and illustrator, John Rocco. *Ask*

? Based on the cover, what do you think this book might be about? (a boy and some robots)

? How do you know? (The boy is reading a book called *3 Little Robots,* and there are three robots on the cover.)

Then read the book aloud.

 **Questioning**

After reading, *ask*

? What kinds of jobs do robots do? (Answers will vary.)

? What job do you think the robots in the book were designed to do? (entertain the boy or take care of the boy; students may notice that the first two-page spread has pictures on the wall showing that the robots have been with the boy since he was a baby)

? Do most robots look like the ones in the book? (Answers will vary.)

explore

Robot Arms

Tell students that most robots look nothing like the cute, funny ones featured in the book *Beep! Beep! Go to Sleep!* In fact, robots that consist of just a moving "arm" are among the most common robots used. Show students the robot arm on pages 22 and 23 of *National Geographic Kids: Robots.* Tell students they are going to do a fun activity to model how one of these robot arms works.

ROBOT ARMS ACTIVITY

Before beginning the activity, divide students into teams of two. Tell students that one member of each pair is going to be the "robot arm" and the other member is going to be the "programmer." (They will be switching roles after the first trial.) Explain that all robots need to be *programmed* to do their job. This means that engineers must write a very specific set of instructions called a *computer program* and then upload, or transfer, the program

to a robot's computer. The student who is the programmer will be reading these instructions to the student who is modeling the robot arm so that this student knows how to do their assigned job. (You may want to read the Robot Program that follows together if your students are not yet reading independently.)

Give a plastic zipper bag of pasta (spirals and either tubes or bowties) and a precut folder (to act as a screen) to each pair. Give a Robot Arm Program Card to each programmer. Then read aloud the directions below:

Directions for Robot Arms Activity

1. Stand the folder on the table. The first person to be the robot should place one hand through the hole in the folder and lean over until their forehead is touching the folder. The robot should not be able to see their own hand (but may use the other hand to keep the folder standing up).

2. The programmer should dump the pasta into a bowl in front of the folder, within reach of the robot arm.

3. The programmer will tell the robot how to do its job by reading a set of instructions called the *Robot Program.*

When all pairs are set up and ready to go, call out, "START!"

Robot Program

1. Pick up a piece of pasta from the bowl.
2. IF the pasta feels like a spiral, THEN place it to the left of the bowl, or ELSE place it to the right of the bowl.
3. IF any pasta is still in the bowl, THEN GO TO step 1, or ELSE END program.

After a few minutes of pasta sorting (or more if necessary), call out, "STOP!" Next, have the programmers remove the folder so their partners can see the results. Then have students trade roles and repeat the activity.

explain

Robot Arms Discussion and Chocolate Factory Video

*Questioning*

> **SEP: Planning and Carrying Out Investigations**
> Make observations of a proposed object or tool to determine if it solves a problem or meets a goal.

After everyone has had a chance to be both a programmer and a robot arm, *ask*

? What problem did the robot arms have to solve? (sort the pasta)

? How well did the robot arms solve the problem? (Answers will vary.)

? Is this a job you would want to do? (Students will most likely answer no.)

? Why or why not? (It would be boring or too repetitive, and your arm would get tired.)

? What parts or structures on the robot arms helped them do their job? (movable elbows, wrists, hands, fingers, etc.)

? Did the programmer ever have to give the robot additional instructions? (Answers will vary.)

Explain that real robots can *only* do what they are programmed to do. Every step of a task must be spelled out in the robot's program. If the program is not detailed and exact, the robot won't be able to do its job very well or at all. Discuss the Robot Program used in the model. Point out that many types of computer programs are similar to this one: They are made up of a series of statements such as IF-THEN and IF-GO TO. You may want to give students the opportunity to write another simple program for a robotic arm, such as a program for sorting and placing different-shaped blocks into containers.

Next, explain that robot arms are typically used in factories, doing jobs that people might not want to do because they are so repetitive (meaning they are repeated over and over). There are many different types of robot arms used in industry. One kind is designed to spray-paint cars. Another kind welds metal together. One of the most common kinds found in factories and warehouses is called a *pick-and-place robot* because it is designed to pick things up and place them somewhere else, usually into some sort of package. The robot arm they modeled is a type of pick-and-place robot.

After completing the Robot Arms activity, tell students that they will have an opportunity to see some real pick-and-place robot arms in action. Introduce the video "M-430iA Robots in Food Industry: 'Pick&Place of Chocolates'" (see the "Websites" section), which features two FANUC Robotics robot arms in a chocolate factory "picking and placing" different kinds of chocolate truffles into blister packs, and have students observe the robot arms doing their jobs.

After watching, point out that these robots have vision sensors, which are cameras that help them "see" the chocolates. Also, explain that although the robots are automatically doing their jobs, a machine operator nearby is controlling the settings on the robots' computers. Robots can only do jobs they are programmed to do, and often their programs need to be changed or adjusted for them to do their job properly.

Connecting to the Common Core
Reading: Informational Text
KEY IDEAS AND DETAILS: 1.1

 **Questioning**

After watching the video, *ask*

? Is packaging chocolate a job that a person could do? (yes)

? Would you want to do that job? (Answers will vary.)

? Why do you think the chocolate factory uses robots instead of people to pick and place chocolates? (The job is boring, it is repetitive, the robots are faster, the robots never get tired, etc.)

Making Connections: Text to Self

Then, help students make connections between the video and the Robot Arms activity. *Ask*

? How were the chocolate factory robot arms like the robot arms we modeled? (They were picking up food and sorting it, they stayed in one place, and they had to be programmed.)

? How were they different? (The factory robots were picking the food from a moving conveyor belt instead of a bowl, they were putting the chocolates into different kinds of packages instead of piles, they could "see" the objects whereas our robots could only feel the objects, they could work a lot faster, etc.)

> **SEP: Developing and Using Models**
> Distinguish between a model and the actual object, process, and/or events the model represents

Tell students that they are going to learn much more about what robots look like and the many kinds of jobs they do.

explain

National Geographic Kids: Robots Read-Aloud

Turn and Talk

Show students the cover of the book *National Geographic Kids: Robots,* and *ask*

? What's a robot? (Students will likely provide a variety of responses—even engineers don't always agree on the definition of *robot.*)

Making Connections: Text to World

Read and discuss pages 4–7, which describe these characteristics of a robot:

- Has movable parts or structures
- Can make decisions
- Is designed by people to do a job by itself

Remind students of the Robot Arms activity. Ask them to think about the pick-and-place robot arm that was programmed to sort the pasta. *Ask*

? If that had been a real robotic arm, and not a kid's arm, would it meet the characteristics of a robot?

Go through each characteristic, asking students to give a thumbs-up or thumbs-down to show whether they think their pick-and-place robot arms meets each characteristic. Then ask them to explain why. *Ask*

? Does it have movable parts or structures? (Yes, the arm moved at the elbow and wrist joints, and the fingers also moved.)

? Can it make decisions? (Yes, when it felt a spiral-shaped piece of pasta, it placed it to the left of the bowl. When the bowl was empty, it stopped.)

? Is it designed by people to do a job by itself? (Yes, it could do the job by itself with the right programming.)

Read pages 10–11 about the parts of a robot, and *ask*

? What part of a robot is like a person's brain? (computer)

? What parts of a robot receive messages from the computer and control the robot's movements? (actuators)

? What parts of a robot collect information about its surroundings? (sensors)

Explain that many robots have vision sensors—cameras that help them "see" and recognize the shapes or even the colors of objects. These sensors help the robot make decisions such as what object to pick up, where to put it, where to paint or weld on a car, and so on. *Ask*

? What kind of sensor did your robot arm have in the pasta sorting activity? (touch)

? What kind of sensors do you think the chocolate factory robots had? (touch, sight, or both)

Making Connections: Text to Text

The little blue robot in *Beep! Beep! Go to Sleep!* said, "My sensor aches!" *Ask*

? What kind of sensor do you think it had? (Answers will vary.)

Robot Jobs Card Sort

Explain that every robot is designed for a specific job, and that job determines what a robot looks like. Tell students that in the book *National Geographic Kids: Robots,* they will learn about the jobs that robots do at work, at home, and in space. Before reading, pass out the Robot Jobs Card Sort and Robot Job Descriptions student pages, and have the students cut out the pictures of the robots. Read each robot job description aloud, and then have students place their cards where they think the cards go. Students will have the opportunity to move their cards as you read the book.

Connecting to the Common Core
Reading: Informational Text
KEY IDEAS AND DETAILS: 1.1

Explain that, because this book is nonfiction, you can enter the text at any point. You don't have to read the book from cover to cover if you are looking for specific information. Tell students that parts of this book will help them match their robot cards with the robot jobs. Ask students to signal (by giving a thumbs-up, making "robot arms," or using some other method) when they see or hear one of the robots from the picture cards. Stop each time you read about a robot from the Robot Jobs Card Sort student page, and have students move their cards if necessary.

 *Chunking*

Follow the steps below to "chunk" the book into the following sections: Robots at Work, Robots at Home, and Robots in Space. Note that you will not read the entire book aloud.

1. Robots at Work: Read pages 22–25, featuring factory robots and the volcano-exploring robot.
2. Robots at Home: Read pages 26–29, featuring the robot alarm clock and the fetch bot.
3. Robots in Space: Read pages 38–41, featuring the robonaut and the Mars rovers.

After reading, students may glue the picture cards onto the Robot Job Descriptions student page once they are all in the correct spaces. The answers to the Robot Jobs Card Sort are as follows:

1. F (Factory Robot)
2. E (Dante II)
3. A (Robot Alarm Clock)
4. C (Fetch Bot)
5. B (Robonaut)
6. D (Curiosity Rover)

 Questioning

After reading, ask students to fill in the blanks as you make the following statements:

? Every robot is designed for a specific _____. (job)

? What a robot looks like depends on _____. (the job it was designed for or built to do)

 Turn and Talk

Ask

? What was your favorite robot in the book? Why? (Answers will vary.)

 Making Connections: Text to Text

Optional: Show students the "What Are Robots?" video listed in the "Websites" section at the end of this lesson. Then have students compare what they learned in the book *National Geographic Kids: Robots* to what they learned in the video.

elaborate

Robots of the Future

Read pages 44–45 about robots of the future. *Ask*

? After learning about robots and the jobs they can do, would you want to be a person who designs or builds robots? (Answers will vary.)

? Would you want a robot in your home? (Students will likely say yes!)

Tell students they are going to have the opportunity to be roboticists—engineers who design, program, and test robots! They will be designing their very own robot with the purpose of solving

a human problem or meeting a human need in their own home or classroom. Tell students that in the not-so-distant future, robots in homes and schools may be commonplace. For inspiration, you can show students the first two-page spread of *Beep! Beep! Go to Sleep!* and have them imagine what it would be like to have a friendly robot in their home or school like the ones pictured.

 **Word Web**

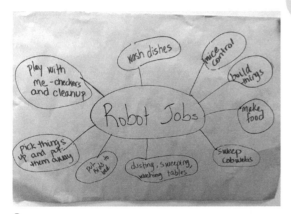

ROBOT JOBS WORD WEB

Next, students can brainstorm jobs a robot could help them do. Make a word web with the target words *Robot Jobs* in the middle, and organize student ideas in circles that surround it. Ask guiding questions, such as the following:

? What are some jobs that you do around your home or at school?

? What tools or machines do you or your families or teachers use to help get the jobs done?

? Are there any jobs that a robot could do around your home or school that you could not do?

? Are there any jobs that a robot could do around your home or school better than you could do them?

? What are some ways that a robot might entertain you or teach you better than another toy or game that you play with?

Then brainstorm some robot ideas together. Examples might include a robot designed to take

out the trash that can carry heavier trash bags than you can carry or that can see in the dark (so it can take out the trash at night); a robot designed to play chess that can teach you to play better than your brother or sister and can also put away the chess pieces when you are finished; or a robot that can feed the classroom fish during weekends or vacations and can give the fish exactly the right amount of food every time.

evaluate

My Robot

Connecting to the Common Core
Writing
TEXT TYPES AND PURPOSES: 1.1

SEP: Developing and Using Models
Develop a simple model based on evidence to represent a proposed object or tool.

SEP: Constructing Explanations and Designing Solutions
Use tools and/or materials to design and/or build a device that solves a specific problem.

Writing

Next, have each student select an idea from your brainstorming session, or come up with an idea of his or her own. Give each student a copy of the My Robot student page. Read the page together.

You may choose to have students use the My Robot Advertisement student page, or have them draw their robot on construction paper or poster board. Students may want to build a non-working

OUR ROBOT DESIGNS

prototype out of boxes or other recycled materials. You can have students present their robots to the class, have a "Robot Exhibition," invite other classes to attend a gallery walk, or display the posters in the classroom or hallway.

STEM Everywhere

Give students the STEM Everywhere student page as a way to involve their families and extend their learning. They can do the activity with an adult helper and share their results with the class. If students do not have access to the internet at home, you may choose to have them complete this activity at school.

Opportunities for Differentiated Instruction

This box lists questions and challenges related to the lesson that students may select to research, investigate, or innovate. Students may also use the questions as examples to help them generate their own questions. These questions can help you move your students from the teacher-directed investigation to engaging in the science and engineering practices in a more student-directed format.

Extra Support

For students who are struggling to meet the lesson objectives, provide a question and guide them in the process of collecting research or helping them design procedures or solutions.

Extensions

For students with high interest or who have already met the lesson objectives, have them choose a question (or pose their own question), conduct their own research, and design their own procedures or solutions.

After selecting one of the questions in this box or formulating their own questions, students can individually or collaboratively make predictions, design investigations or surveys to test their predictions, collect evidence, devise explanations, design solutions, or examine related resources. They can communicate their findings through a science notebook, at a poster session or gallery walk, or by producing a media project.

Research

Have students brainstorm researchable questions:

? What is the world's largest walking robot?

? How did the Mars rovers get onto the surface of Mars?

? What is biomimicry, and what are some examples of it in robot design?

Continued

Opportunities for Differentiated Instruction (continued)

Investigate

Have students brainstorm testable questions to be solved through science or math:

? How many pieces of pasta can your partner's "robot arm" sort in 1 minute without looking?

? Survey your friends: Would you want to have a robot take care of you if you were sick, or would you prefer a human nurse? Graph the results, then analyze your graph. What can you conclude?

? Survey your friends: What household chore would you most want a robot to do? Graph the results, then analyze your graph. What can you conclude?

Innovate

Have students brainstorm problems to be solved through engineering:

? Can you write a code to program your partner's "robotic arm" to sort blocks by their shape or color?

? What kind of robot would you design to help you at school?

? What kind of robot would you design to explore a volcano, the deep ocean, or outer space?

Websites

 "M-430iA Robots in Food Industry: 'Pick&Place' of Chocolates" (video) *www.youtube.com/watch?v=ZSbFW_ ncIdU*

 "What Are Robots?" (video) *https://cet.pbslearningmedia.org/ resource/98c171a8-d8c5-446b-a5e1- a1d10abf424c/what-are-robots-young- explorers*

More Books to Read

Fliess, S. 2013. *Robots, robots, everywhere.* New York: Golden Books.
Summary: This delightful rhyming picture book for very young readers features robots of all kinds, from the ones in space to the ones we use at home.

Funk, J. 2018. *How to code a sandcastle.* New York: Viking Books for Young Readers.
Summary: This entertaining picture book for young readers introduces the basics of coding in a fun and accessible way.

Funk, J. 2019. *How to code a rollercoaster.* New York: Viking Books for Young Readers.
Summary: This follow-up to *How to Code a Sand-castle* continues the adventures of two characters who use code to navigate their way through challenging situations.

Shulman, M. 2014. *TIME for Kids: Explorers—Robots.* New York: TIME for Kids.
Summary: Full of facts and photos, this book in the popular *TIME for Kids* series shows young readers just how useful robots are and why we need them.

Swanson, J. 2016. *National Geographic Kids: Everything robotics—All the photos, facts, and fun to make you race for robots.* Washington, DC: National Geographic Children's Books.
Summary: With stunning visuals and an energetic design, this book for older readers (grades 3–7) reveals everything kids want to know about robotics.

Van Dusen, C. 2016. *Randy Riley's really big hit.* Somerville, MA: Candlewick Press.
Summary: This lively rhyming book tells the tale of Randy Riley, a boy who loves both science and baseball. When he spies a massive fireball in space headed to his town, he uses his robotics skills to save the day.

Robot Arm Program Cards

ROBOT PROGRAM

1. Pick up a piece of pasta from the bowl.

2. IF the pasta feels like a spiral, THEN place it to the left of the bowl, or ELSE place it to the right of the bowl.

3. IF any pasta is still in the bowl, THEN GO TO step 1, or ELSE END program.

ROBOT PROGRAM

1. Pick up a piece of pasta from the bowl.

2. IF the pasta feels like a spiral, THEN place it to the left of the bowl, or ELSE place it to the right of the bowl.

3. IF any pasta is still in the bowl, THEN GO TO step 1, or ELSE END program.

National Science Teaching Association

Robot Jobs Card Sort

Robots do many different kinds of jobs. They often do jobs that people don't want to do or can't do. What a robot looks like depends on the job it was designed to do.

Directions: Cut out the robot cards below and match each robot to its job description on the Robot Job Descriptions page. Then listen as your teacher reads the book *National Geographic Kids: Robots*. You will have the chance to move the cards again as your teacher reads the book.

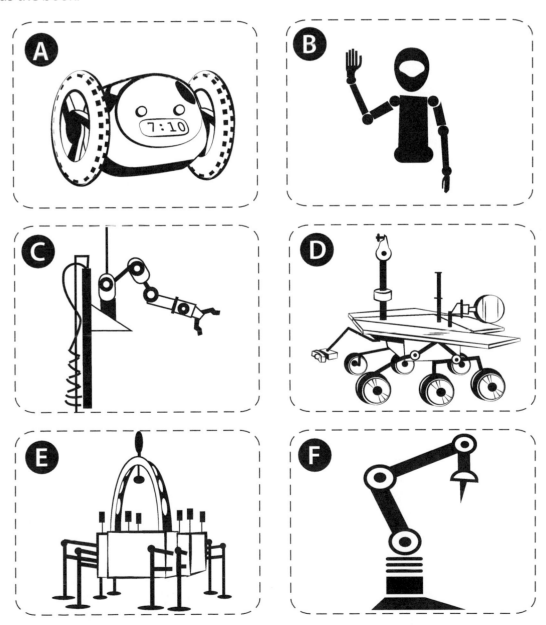

Name: _____

Robot Job Descriptions

Match the robot picture with the right description.

1 This robot arm welds together metal parts in a factory.

2 This eight-legged robot was designed to explore an active volcano.

3 This robot alarm clock is on wheels and rolls around your room.

4 This robot can pick up an object you want and bring it to you.

5 This humanlike robot works on the International Space Station.

6 This six-wheeled robot was designed to explore the surface of Mars.

Name: _____

My Robot

Challenge: Design a robot to do a job in your home or classroom.

Robot's name: _____

Robot's job: _____

_____

Think about how your robot can do the job better than a person could do it or how it can do the job better than another technology. Then list some reasons that people should buy your robot.

_____

_____

_____

_____

_____

_____

_____

Now, draw your robot and create an advertisement to sell it! Include the robot's name and its job, and label the parts of your robot that help it do its job.

Name: _____

My Robot Advertisement

National Science Teaching Association

Name: _____

STEM Everywhere

Dear Families,

At school, we have been learning about **robots.** We learned that every robot is designed for a specific job, and that job determines what a robot looks like. To find out more, ask your learner the following questions and discuss their answers:

- What did you learn?

- What was your favorite part of the lesson?

- What are you still wondering?

At home, you can watch a short video together called "Sandeep Yayathi: Robotics Engineer" about Robonaut 2, or R2, a humanlike robot designed to assist astronauts in space.

 Scan the QR code; go to *www.pbslearningmedia.org* and search "Sandeep Yayathi: Robotics Engineer"; or go to *http://cet. pbslearningmedia.org/resource/mss13.sci.engin.design.robeng/ sandeep-yayathi-robotics-engineer.*

If you were a robotics engineer, what kinds of robots would you want to design and why? (Write or draw)